Learning Grammar with Drama 2

Learning Grammar with Drama 2

발 행 | 2024년 07월 03일
저 자 | Dinka Hernández Avilés
펴낸이 | 한건희
펴낸곳 | 주식회사 부크크
출판사등록 | 2014.07.15(제2014-16호)
주 소 | 서울특별시 금천구 가산디지털1로 119 SK트윈타워 A동 305호
전 화 | 1670-8316
이메일 | info@bookk.co.kr

ISBN | 979-11-410-9261-0

www.bookk.co.kr

SPECIAL THANKS

For starters, my wonderful mother, Veronica, who has never stopped supporting me and encouraging me. I would not be where I am today if it was not for her.

To my grandmothers, Dinka and Rosa, who are no longer physically with me but I know their souls walk with me everyday.

To my amazing friends, Sofia, Maria, Jessica, Megan, Jiseon and Luna, for always being there for me and putting a smile on my face when I have needed it.

To Professors Teresa and Sujeong, who showed me the fascinating world of Drama in the classroom.

To my students, you are the reason I love my job: Kate, James, Ah-In, Seon, Jay, P. Jay, Jayden, Lucy, Emma, Luke, Simba, Chaeny, big Luke, Charlotte, Bella, Jun, Hai, Roan, Seoho, Minji, Celine, Yeonsu, Yoon, Ha-Im, Erena, Seoyun, and Sofia. Thank you for allowing me to be your teacher and for always making me part of your adventures.

To Lizzy for her support and for valuing my skills and knowldege.

To God and the Universe for always having my back.

Last but not least, I want to thank me; for never giving up despite all the storms unleashed in my way, for believing in myself that I can make things happen, and for becoming the woman I always dreamed to be.

TABLE OF CONTENTS

INTRODUCTION:
WHY LEARNING GRAMMAR WITH DRAMA?

Learning grammar can be quite a monotonous and tortous experience for most students since they have to learn all these bunch of rules and uses in a whole different language. However, it can also present a difficulty for teachers who love bringing interaction and dynamism to the classroom, which most of the time is hard since they have to follow a book that only allows them to work in a pretty conventional classroom setting: the teacher in the front, the students sitting and working on their books.

Therefore in my vast experience as an English teacher, especially as an English teacher in South Korea, along with my academic knowledge acquisition, I have come up with the idea that it is always possible to bring fun into the classroom, no matter what age of the students.

Thus, I have developed this book series as a way to aid teachers to bring that spark into the classroom and make something that seems so boring and challenging, into something that can also be exciting and fun.

I hope you have fun using this book as much as I did writing it.

MESSAGE TO EDUCATORS

My dear fellow teachers:

I hope that when you get in the classroom you can feel that there, in front of your eyes, lays the future. All those lovely little monkeys are the tomorrow and what you do in the classroom does impact what they will become.

I hope you know that you are forming people and not machines, and as so I hope you can find value in such resources as imagination, creativity and play. That is why I created this book, to make it slightly easier for you to use these skills as assets for conveying knowledge. I truly hope you can get fascinated with the outcomes as I did when I started to put this method into practice.

I wish you the best of luck!

ABOUT THE AUTHOR

Dinka Yolanda Hernández Avilés is a Chilean psychologist, who has been working in the education field for 6 years. She has experience teaching languages (English and Spanish) in her country, Chile, as well as in South Korea and China. She has also worked as a content writer for a humanitarian company in Turkey, as well as a volunteer psychologist at YMCA-Europe offering services for victims of the Russian- Ukrainian conflict. Currently, she is pursuing her Master's degree in ESL at IGSE in South Korea.

SYLLABUS

Unit 1	The fun is always in place!	Goal
Warm-Up	Categorization Game	• For students to activate prior knowledge. • For students to identify prepositions of place: *inside, on, next to, between and under.*
Let's Practice!	Map Adventure	• For students to practice the spoken form of prepositions of place.
Your Turn!	Directional Drawing	• For students to make use of prepositions of place in an active and creative way.

Unit 2	Laughing in the face o f time	Goal
Warm-Up	Time Fill-in the Blanks	• For students to review prior content. • For students to practice prepositions of time: *at, on, in, before, after.*
Let's Practice!	Make Sentences	• For students to practice correct use of prepositions of time. • For students to practice writing.
Your Turn!	Timed Storytelling	• For students to produce a story by using the proper prepositions of time.

SYLLABUS

Unit 3	Verb-A-Palooza: Present Simple	Goal
Warm-Up	Describe	• For students to identify simple present sentence structure. • For students to practice the written form of simple present sentence structure.
	Adverbs of Frquency	• For students to recognize and practice the correct form and use of *always, usually, often, sometimes, rarely, never.*
Let's Practice!	Present Simple Pantomime	• To challenge students to practice making sentences using the tense orally.
Your Turn!	Daily Routine Skits	• To consolidate knowledge by producing a creative writing task using the tense.

Unit 4	I'm better than and the best at: comparatives and superlatives	Goal
Warm-Up	Sentence Finisher	• For students to activate prior knowledge. • For students to practice the written form of comparative/ superlative adjectives.
Let's Practice!	Comparative Situations	• For students to practice proper use of adjectives in their comparative form (*-er than*)
Your Turn!	Superlative Commercial	• For students to practice proper use of adjectives in their superlative form (*the -st*)

SYLLABUS

Unit 5	What did I do..? Past Simple	Goal
Warm-Up	Verbs	• For students to remember prior contents. • For students to practice the correct past form of the verbs (*regulars e irregulars*).
Let's Practice!	Memory Lane Interview	• For students to make use of past tense form (*question, positive, negative*)
Your Turn!	Time Machine Improv	• To use past tense in a creative context.

Unit 6	What about tomorrow? Future Simple	Goal
Warm-Up	Guess the Future	• For students to recognize and practice future tense sentences.
Let's Practice!	Future Fortune Teller	• For students to practice both written and spoken form of Future Simple sentences. • To enhance confidence by interacting using the target language.
Your Turn!	Future Superhero Adventure	• For students to consolidate the grammar point knowledge in a creative way.

SYLLABUS

Unit 7	What is Happening Now? Present Progressive).	Goal
Warm-Up	Living Picture Album	• To practice the correct use Present Progressive sentence form.
Let's Practice!	Moving Statues	• To gain further practice and confidence using the language form.
Your Turn!	Progressive Role Swap	• To produce the language using the target grammar point in an imaginative context.

Unit 8	I'm going to... Future (going to)	Goal
Warm-Up	Vacation Planning Improv	• For students to practice the spoken form of *future (going to)*.
Let's Practice!	Weather Forecast Skits	• For students to practice the written form of *future (going to)*.
Your Turn!	School Year Predictions	• For students to consolidate the correct use of *future (going to)* in an engaging and freer way.

SYLLABUS

Unit 9	Past Continous	Goal
Warm-Up	Guess the Aaction Mime	• To practice the correct use of past continuos in its spoken form.
Let's Practice!	News Reporter Flashback	• To practice the written form of past progressive • To gaing further confidence using the spoken form of the tense into longer sentences.
Your Turn!	Camping Adventure	• To produce the language using the target grammar point in an imaginative context.

UNIT 1: THE FUN IS ALWAYS IN PLACE!

(Prepositions of place)

Warm-up

Categorization Game: Cut the cards on page 46. Clasify them into inside, on, next to, between and under.

inside	
on	
next to	
between	
under	

act:
do something,
perform

Let's
Practice!

Map Adventure: Get in couples and create a map of any place you want (real or imaginary). Then, one member describes the place while the other members acts it. For example, "The castle is on the hill. The treasure chest is next to the castle."

Your Turn!

Directional Drawing: Work in couples. Give seach other simple instructions to draw a picture using prepositions of place. For example, "Draw a cat under the table" or "Draw a sun between the two mountains." Then act it out and the audience has to guess what your drawing is about.

Draw here what your classmate tells you:

Write here the instructions for your classmate:

_____

_____

_____

_____

_____

_____

UNIT 2: LAUGHING IN THE FACE OF TIME

(Prepositions of time)

Warm-up

Time Fill-in-the-Blanks: Look at the sentences below. They have missing time prepositions. Fill in with the correct one: **at, on, in, before, after.**

1) I have a meeting _____Monday morning.

2) She eats dinner _____work.

3) My birthday is _____ December.

4) The class starts _____ noon.

5) I wake up _____ 8 AM.

6) I brush my teeth _____ going to school.

appropiate: correct

Let's Practice!

Make sentences: Look at the different prepositions of time below. Write sentences using the appropiate time prepositions to describe things that you do everyday. Then in groups, use tableau (frozen image) to act the different sentences you created and the other members have to guess. For example: *"I go to school in the morning"*

In the morning/ afternoon   after

At noon

on

before

Here are some ideas you can use!

Timed Storytelling: Work in groups. Look at the following pictures and create a story using prepositions of time. Then, act your stories while the audience says sentences using preposirions of time. Make a funny and creative story!

The audience should say things like: *"He wakes up at 8 AM/ He walks to school in the morning, ..."*

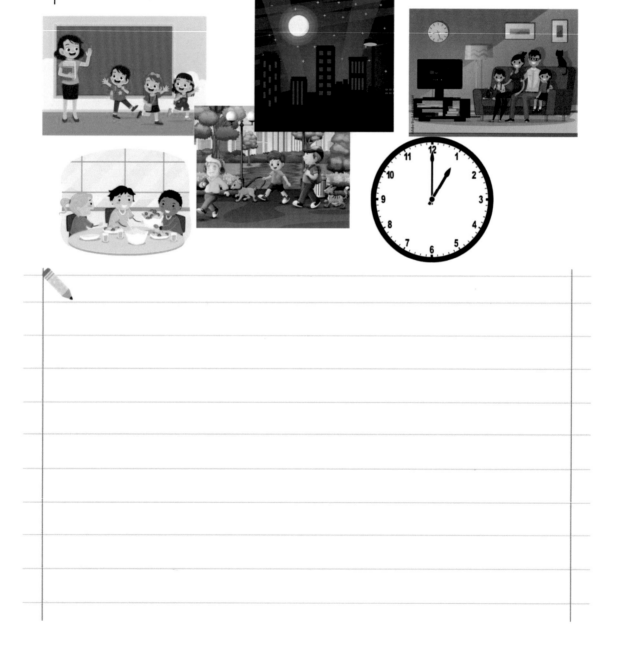

UNIT 3: VERB-A-PALOOZA: PRESENT SIMPLE

Warm-up

Describe: Look at the picture below. Describe what you see using sentences in present simple.

ex. A boy paints

Adverbs of frequency: Choose the correct adverb for each picture and make a sentence.

0%	20%	40%	60%	80%	100%
never	rarely	sometimes	often	usually	always

Warm-up

She sometimes plays the guitar

• • • • • • • • • • • • • •

• • • • • • • • • • • • • •

• • • • • • • • • • • • •

• • • • • • • • • • • • •

• • • • • • • • • • • • •

• • • • • • • • • • • • •

Let's Practice!

Present Simple Pantomime: Everybody get in groups. Cut the cards on pages 47-49. Then get in lines; member by member come to the front, pick one card and act what you read on it. The rest of the group members must guess using the correct sentence in present simple. For example; *"She walks the dog"* or *"He eats pizza"*. *The group with the most correct guesses, wins*!

I GIVE THIS ACTIVITY:

MY FAVORITE PART WAS:

Daily Routine Skits: work in small groups to create short skits that depict a typical day in someone's life.

Each group should focus on using the present simple tense to describe routines and habits.

Groups then perform their skits for the class.

Your turn!

For example: *John wakes up at 7:30 am. Then, he takes a shower a has breakfast...*

UNIT 4
I'M BETTER THAN AND THE BEST AT: COMPARATIVES AND SUPERLATIVES

Warm-up

Sentence Finisher: Look at these sentences; they have a blank space for either a comparative or superlative form of an adjective.

In pairs, consider the adjectives in the box and choose the most appropiate one for each sentence. Remember to change their form if necessary.

Then, share your answers with the class and compare them.

| large | healthy | tall | deep | fast | hot | cold |

The new smartphone is _____ _____ the previous model.

This mountain is _____ _____ any peak in the surrounding range.

The blue whale is the _____ mammal on Earth.

Running is _____ _____ sitting on the couch all day.

The winter weather in Alaska is _____ _____ in Florida.

The Sahara Desert is the _____ desert in the world.

The Grand Canyon is one of the _____ canyons in the world.

Comparative Situations: Get in groups. Choose one of the following scenarios; improvise a dialogue using comparatives to express your opinions and preferences. Then, perform it for your class.

Let's Practice!

| winter v/s summer | English v/s math |

| hamburger v/s pizza | cat v/s dog |

Follow the example:

_____: "_____ is better than _____, because..."

_____: "I disagree. I think _____ is better than _____, because ..."

Make your notes here:

Superlative Commercial Challenge: Create and perform a commercial for a fictional product that is the "best" or "most amazing" in its category. Use superlatives to convince the audience of the product's superiority.

Follow the example:

Your turn!

> Narrator: "Introducing the AmazingTech WonderBox – the **best** way to make your everyday life even more fantastic! Why settle for good when you can have the **greatest**?"...

UNIT 5: WHAT DID I DO..? PAST SIMPLE

Warm-up

Verbs: Write the correct past form of the verbs below the different pictures. Choose one verb, create a sentence and perform it to the audience so they can guess the correct sentence.

went

memorable: unforgettable, special

Memory Lane Interview: In pairs, interview each other about a memorable experience using past simple questions (e.g., *"What did you do last summer?"*).

Then present your partner's story to the class in an interview format.

Let's Practice!

Write the questns for your partner in here!

historical: something or someone important from the past

Time Machine Improv: Imagine you have a time machine that can take you to any historical event.

Get in groups and improvise scenes from the past, using past simple verbs to describe your actions and experiences. USE YOUR IMAGINATION!

Your turn!

Take notes here!

UNIT 6: WHAT ABOUT TOMORROW? FUTURE SIMPLE

common:
usual, normal

Guess the Future:

In the back of your book (pp. 50-52), there are cards with simple future tense sentences describing common activities. Get in groups, and in relay race fashion, pick a card, act out the sentence without speaking, while your classmates guess the action.

Warm-up

I GIVE THIS ACTIVITY:

MY FAVORITE PART WAS:

Let's
Practice!

Future Fortune Teller: Get in pairs. Take on the role of fortune tellers and predict your classmates' futures using the future simple tense.

Then create short scenes or monologues based on predictions about future achievements, travels, or experiences

Travels

Achievements

Experiences, etc...

Future Superhero Adventure: Create and act out a short superhero skit where you use your superpowers to solve a future problem.

Use the future simple tense to describe your superhero actions.

Your turn!

Write your superhero name

Draw your costume here!

UNIT 7: WHAT IS HAPPENING NOW? PRESENT PROGRESSIVE

Warm-up

Living Picture Album: Get in groups. Look at the picture-cards in the back of your book (pp. 53-54) Cut them, and create a short story. Create "living pictures" by freezing in a pose that represents the sentence while others guess the action and the story.

Glue the pictures here!

Write your notes here!

Moving Statues: Move around the room (the teacher can play some music in the background). Anyone can call out a verb in present progressive (*eg. swimming*), and everybody must freeze in a pose representing that action.

Let's Practice!

I GIVE THIS ACTIVITY:

MY FAVORITE PART WAS:

scenario: situation, scene

Progressive Role Swap: Get in pairs and choose one of the scenarios below. Act out the scenario, taking turns playing different roles and describing ongoing actions.

☀ **Your turn!**

at the doctor's office	at the restaurant
at the airport	at the police station
at the Café	at the zoo

Write your notes here!

UNIT 8: I'M GOING TO... FUTURE (GOING TO)

Warm-up

Vacation Planning Improv: Get in groups and plan an imaginary vacation. Use "going to" to discuss and improvise scenes about activities, sights, and experiences you are going to have on your vacation.

Weather Forecast Skits: Imagine you become a weather forecaster. Predict future weather conditions using "going to" to describe the weather for different days in a skit, incorporating gestures and expressions to enhance the performance

	MON	TUE	WED	THU

On Monday it's going to...

School Year Predictions: Get in groups. Discuss and act out scenes related to your predictions for the upcoming school year. Use "going to" to express your expectations and plans for the academic year.

Your turn!

Next year, the school is going to...

UNIT 9:
PAST CONTINUOUS

Warm-up

Guess the Action Mime: Look at the back of your book (pp. 55-57). Cut the cards, get in groups, one by one take turns and act one of the actions pointed on the cards while the other members have to guess the correct action. The first member that guesses correctly, removes the card from their stack. The first member to be left with no cards, wins!

I GIVE THIS ACTIVITY:

MY FAVORITE PART WAS:

News Reporter Flashback: Take turns being news reporters describing past events. Use past continuous sentences to report on specific actions during those events.

Let's Practice!

Describe here the event you will report!

Title of the event:

describe: tell of, report

Camping Adventure: Get in couples. Imagine a camping trip and create scenes describing activities during the trip using the past continuous tense.

Act out scenes of setting up tents, cooking, and exploring nature.

Your turn!

Write notes of your scene in here!

FINAL PROJECT IDEAS

Now that you have finished this book, I hope you were able to master these **new** grammar points. In order to prove so, it can be a great idea to have a final project where you can make use of everything you learned. Do you accept the challenge? (The teacher will help you all the time! So ask as much as you want)

Project Idea 1: Story Mural

Get in groups of 4 or 5. On a large piece of paper provided by the teacher, each one of you will draw whatever pictures, shapes, images that come through your mind. ANYTHING. You don't need to arrange what to draw; just simply draw all the random things that come to your mind. Use different colors. You can complement your classmates drawings, ALWAYS WITH RESPECT, by asking the question: "Can I intervene your drawing?"

Here are some examples of murals:

The idea is that while you are drawing, you do not share or pact with your classmates what will you draw; you just draw, throw lines, color, or write whatever comes to your mind. You will have around 20 minutes to do this.

After you are done, based on the final product, you and your classmates will create a story based on the drawings you made. Once you are done with the story, you and your group will present your mural and read the story you created.

Here you have lines to write your story.

Here you have lines to write your story.

Here you have lines to write your story.

Here you have lines to write your story.

FINAL PROJECT IDEAS

Project Idea 2: Create a pantomime act.

With your group, create a short pantomime act based on one of the three tittles below. Create the story, assign characters and practice the scenes.

A pantomime is representing or expressing something by using gestures and body movements. In a pantomime, we do not make any sounds, how fun!

Lost in Neverland: A Pantomime Adveture

Pantomime Pirates: Treasure Island Adventure

The Enchanted Forest: A Pantomime Quest

Here you have lines to write your act.

Here you have lines to write your act.

APPENDIX: MATERIALS

✂ **Unit 1: Warm up - Categorization Game**

  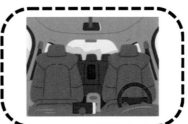

APPENDIX: MATERIALS

Unit 3: Let's practice - Present Simple Pantomime

She goes to school	They wait for the food
I feel sad	He cleans the room
You eat breakfast at 7 a.m.	She works as a teacher

APPENDIX: MATERIALS

 Unit 3: Let's practice - Present Simple Pantomime

I like to read books	They study English at school
He doesn't eat meat	She watches TV
He plays the guitar	I don't like coffee

APPENDIX: MATERIALS

Unit 3: Let's practice - Present Simple Pantomime (add your own sentences)

APPENDIX: MATERIALS

 Unit 6: Warm-up - Guess the future

She will eat pizza for dinner	**They study English at school**
He will study English after school	**She will buy a new dress for the party.**
We will have a picnic in the park	**Tomorrow, I will clean my room**

APPENDIX: MATERIALS

 Unit 6: Warm-up - Guess the future

She will bake a cake for her birthday.

I will read a book tonight

Today she will go swimming

They will visit the zoo next Sunday.

He will buy a new car next month

We will have ice cream for dessert

APPENDIX: MATERIALS

Unit 6: Warm-up - Guess the future (add your own sentences)

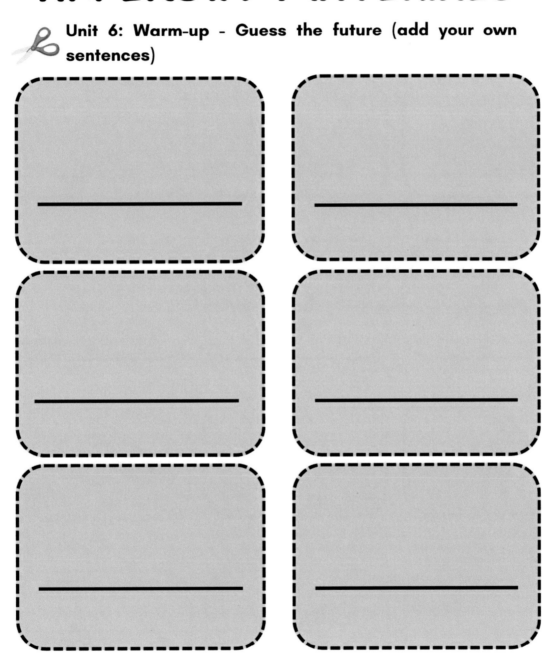

APPENDIX: MATERIALS

✂ **Unit 7: Warm-up - Living Picture Album**

APPENDIX: MATERIALS

Unit 7: Warm-up - Living Picture Album (add your own drawings)

APPENDIX: MATERIALS

 Unit 9: Warm-up - Guess the Action Mime

I was watching TV	They were playing football
She was studying hard	We were having dinner
The baby was crying	She was baking cookies

APPENDIX: MATERIALS

 Unit 9: Warm-up - Guess the Action Mime

The birds were singing

They study English at school

The painter was painting

She watches TV

The cat was chasing a mouse

He was taking pictures

APPENDIX: MATERIALS

Unit 6: Warm-up - Guess the future (add your own sentences)

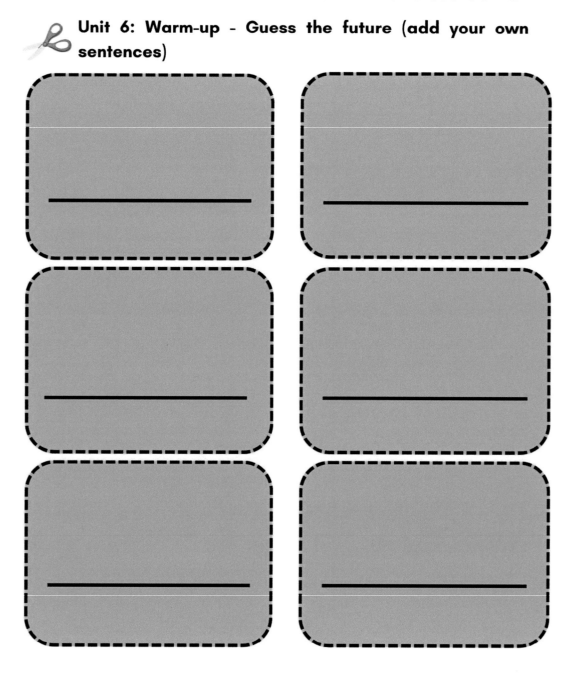

Honest:
Say the truth

SELF EVALUATION

And... here is the end of this book! You have made an amazing job. I hope you had fun while learning these important grammar points. Now, it is time to be very HONEST, and check how much did you learn.

Can I...?	Yes, I can	I can, but I need more practice	No, I cannot
Recognize, identify, and use action verbs			
Make a simple sentence			
Understand and use pronouns			
Recognize and use nouns			
Recognize and use adjectives			
Recognize and use the correct articles			
Recognize and understand singular and plural nouns			
Ask questions using Wh words			

Make a final comment:

THANK YOU FOR USING THIS BOOK, SEE YOU IN THE NEXT LEVEL!

EPILOGUE

As you witnessed through the different units present in this book, the main goal of each unit was for students to make actual use of the grammar point they were learning. And of course, the demand and difficulty of activities increase through the passing of units.

As I mentioned on the prior page, I will see you again in the next book! Because that is right... Learning Grammar with Drama is a book series!

And this is not the end of it! I am planning to extend drama techniques into other language areas and contents! I hope I can meet you there too. Until then!